OTHER BOOKS BY WALT KELLY

TEN EVER-LOVIN' BLUE-EYED YEARS WITH POGO

* * *

DECK US ALL WITH BOSTON CHARLIE

POGO PUCE STAMP CATALOG

INSTANT POGO	THE POGO PARTY
GONE POGO	THE POGO SUNDAY BOOK
POGO À LA SUNDAE	POTLUCK POGO
POGO EXTRA	POGO PEEK-A-BOOK
BEAU POGO	THE INCOMPLEAT POGO
THE POGO SUNDAY BRUNCH	THE POGO STEPMOTHER GOOSE
G. O. FIZZICKLE POGO	THE POGO PAPERS
THE POGO SUNDAY PARADE	UNCLE POGO SO-SO STORIES
POSITIVELY POGO	I GO POGO
POGO'S SUNDAY PUNCH	POGO

* * *

SONGS OF THE POGO   POGOMOBILE

* * *

In collaboration with Pogo

THE JACK ACID SOCIETY BLACK BOOK

The RETURN of POGO

WALT KELLY

SIMON AND SCHUSTER · NEW YORK · 1965

All rights reserved
including the right of reproduction
in whole or in part in any form
Copyright © 1963, 1964, 1965 by Walt Kelly
Published by Simon and Schuster, Inc.
Rockefeller Center, 630 Fifth Avenue
New York, N.Y. 10020

SECOND PRINTING

Library of Congress Catalog Card Number: 65-26385
Manufactured in the United States of America

This book, such as it is,
is for Breslin, such
as he is, with the hope
he will enjoy the pictures,
much as they are...

"The eggs are
up ahead, Sir."

Contents

Culture

IF SUCCESS *consists of reaching your goals, there are a lot of successful young people rampant in these days. It should be pointed out, of course, that they have a low success threshold. If your goals are low, you can reach up and touch them from a slouch position on a lounge. Like the Arab Empire of several centuries ago, a good hunk of the modern flash has decided that the plateau achieved is indeed Mt. Everest.*

These people have, then, fifty or sixty years ahead of them of accumulated rubber-stamp folksongs, touch-me-not dancing, and odds and ends of rubbish flying about, obscuring their vision, as trash in a no-gravity space capsule. It is hard to figure out a generation that believes in contact lenses and non-contact frug.

But as a good reporter, Tom Wolfe, has pointed out, these things, like handmade custom cars, are part of our culture. It makes a lot of us yearn for the good old days of crooked politics, dirty jokes, war and segregation, all of which are now, naturally, in the past. Some of our folkways, our culture, are parodied in the pages yonder—parodies trying to say to the people who believe in the non-tomorrow that Christmas is a year round tomorrow, a fact that goes unnoticed by he who is more interested in the present than in that Christmas.

W.K., 1965

Part One

Forward to the End

I've always thought, in
   the crispness of Noon,
The best of the week
   is Christmas in June.
Then if ever's
   the Ismuth too soon
As we sprinkle and wrinkle
   the Bismuth in tune ---

The Mind Reals, the Memory Quakes

A Perfect Brick
of a Ghost

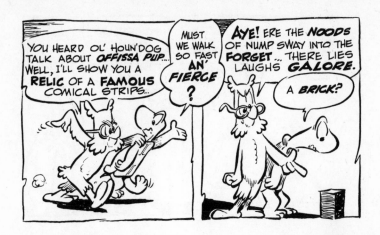

19

Part Two

The Rassle of Beauty

If your eyes
   have made the scene,
Then Beauty has
   a gift serene.
The duty of
   the Human Bean
Is, truly, Toby,
   to be seen ---

Beauty Is Knife Deep

26

The Muscular Side of Loveliness

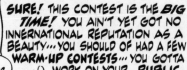

IF YOU'RE GONNA BE IN THE MISS COSMOS BEAUTY CONTEST, YOU'LL HAFTA GET TO WORK.

WORK?

SURE! THIS CONTEST IS THE BIG TIME! YOU AIN'T YET GOT NO INNERNATIONAL REPUTATION AS A BEAUTY... YOU SHOULD OF HAD A FEW WARM-UP CONTESTS... YOU GOTTA WORK ON YOUR PUBLIC IMAGE!

HMMM.... GOTTA WORK ON MY PUBLIC IMAGE....

MIZ BEAVER

THE PRIVATE IMAGE COULD STAND A LITTLE WORK, TOO.

WHAT'S THIS I HEAR 'BOUT YOU STAGIN' A MISS COSMOS BEAUTY CONTEST, HOWLAND?

ANYTHING YOU HEAR IS RIGHT... IT'S THE MOST!

YOU NEED A ORGANIZATION TO JAZZ UP A JOB LIKE THAT...

AN' WE GOT THE BEST!

29

30

Connie-Sewers of Pulchertood

IF YOU'RE LOOKIN' FOR *JUDGES* FOR THE BEAUTY-CONTEST, MEBBE YOU BETTER *SHOP AROUND* A LITTLE...

GOOD IDEA

HI, MOLESTER P. MOLE! WE'RE LOOKIN' FOR A COUPLE OF HONEST JUDGES FOR THE BIG BEAUTY CONTEST.

WHAT KIND BEAUTY CONTEST?

OWL'S RUNNIN' IT... FOR THE TITLE OF *MISS COSMOS*... IT'S LIKE A BIG *INTERPLANETARY* BEAUTY FIGHT TO SEE WHO'S THE HUMDINGER OF *ALL CREATION.*

INTERPLANETARY, EH? WELL, I SUPPOSE THERE'S NO HARM IN THAT, *PROVIDING* THAT NO *FOREIGNERS* ARE ALLOWED IN THE CONTEST *NOR* ARE ALLOWED TO SIT IN JUDGEMENT.

WELL, ONWARD ON OUR DOUBLE-BARRELED DIOGENICAL QUEST...

FORWARD!

AN *INTERPLANETARY* BATHING BEAUTY COMPETITION... *HMMMM* ...

Molester! Old friend! Delightful!

HUSH! DON'T INTERRUPT! NOT A MOMENT TO LOSE!

34

Judge Not Lest You Be Jugged

36

The Be-knighting of the Judges

IT GIVES ME GREAT PLEASURE, MEN, TO INTRUST TO TWO SUCH *JUST JUDGES,* A LIST OF THE *LADIES* AN' THE *STATES* THEY'LL REPERSENT···· AN' A *SEALED ENVELOPE* WHICH YOU WILL OPEN AS YOU BEGIN YOUR *JUDGEMENT*····

WHAT'S IN THE *ENVELOPE?*

THE NAME OF THE WINNER

OWL SAY THE ENVELOPE CONTAIN THE NAME OF THE WINNER.

WHAT'S *WE* GONE BE *JUDGES* FOR?

THAT'S OWL'S ORGANIZATIONAL *GENIUS*····HE LEAVES *NOTHIN'* TO CHANCE····S'POSE WE COULDN'T MAKE UP OUR MINDS WHO'S *MOST PERTY?*

YEH!

A CATASTROPHE! BUT OWL PREVENTS IT BY PICKIN' THE WINNER IN ADVANCE! *BRILLIANT!*

RIGHT! I'M GONNA *PEEK* AN' SEE WHO IT IS····

NO, *DON'T!* THAT WOULDN'T BE *FAIR!*

GUESS YOU'RE *RIGHT.* US JUDGES SHOULD BE AS *SURPRISED* AS ANYBODY.

41

42

44

The Be-knightingale of Goo-Foff

46

48

Part Three

All the Latest
that Laps the Lip

A nose for news
    shall ever blow
In spite of sleet,
    in spite of snow.
Who bites the dog?
    I'd like to know,
When words of naught
    are fraught with flow.

A Double-Headed Hydra Phobia

As a ex-beauty contest judge, I gotta say that even with two heads, this Russian dog ain't twice as perty as any thing.... 'Course, I wouldn't say it to her face....

Man, you'd have a weird time tryin' to say it behind her back!

I'm from the Fort Mudge Moan, the Alert Daily here in the swamp.... I'm after a dog story here.... Ain't no story if you ever bit a man.... But there is one if a man bit you.... Did he?

Nyet

Нет

See, I tole you....They ain't no story in a two-headed dog....Nobody bit him....

If I need dark-room advice, I'll ask.

Hole steady, Pogo....I needs a good, flat surface for this shot....Hey, dog! Smile! Say "cheese"!

Сыр Творог

Man, that dog, or them dogs, never must of heard of cheese....What good's a two-headed dog, anyway?

The Press Presses On

BEFORE ME, THE EDITOR, INTERVIEWS THE **GENUINE EYE-WITNESS REPORTER** HERE, LET'S SEE THE PHOTOS YOU TOOK OF THE **TWO-HEADED DOG**....

SURE THING, CHIEF! TOOK 'EM WITH MY **INSTANTO-PRINT CAMERA** ....LESSEE..."YEP, UH, WE GOT THE **GOODS** RIGHT HERE"... BEST THING ABOUT A **NEWS-PAPER!**

WE GIVES YOU A **PERMANENT RECORD** · **NO FLEETING IMPRESSION OF HISTORY IN THE MAKING**....BUT A SURE THING.... THE **EVER-LASTIN' PHOTO ON PAPER** ....HM...YOU STILL GOT THAT **PENCIL**, CHIEF?

I BETTER **DRAW** YOU A PICTURE OF THIS DOG.... SEEM LIKE I LEFT THE **LENS-CAP** ON THE CAMERA....

WHAT FOR?

NOW, LEMME JUST **DRAW** HOW THIS **TWO-HEADED DOG** LOOKED ....HE HAD A HEAD ON **THIS** END AN' THEN....

HE ...UM... HAD A LEG.... THEN **ANOTHER** LEG ....THEN HE ....UM... HAD A .... MMM... OOF...**ANOTHER**....

....**HEAD ON THE OTHER END! NO?!**

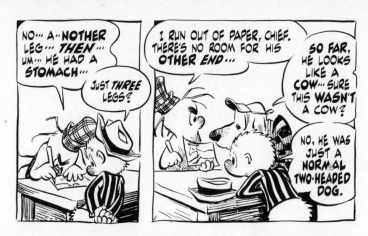

59

It Says Here the Hear Says

OH, YES, HERE IT IS, MEN! BUT FIRST, THIS TIMELY TIP! DUM DUM DUM ♪ OH, DOES YOUR BREAKFAST COME IN *QUARTS?* THEN YOU ARE ENJOYING *WARTS!* WARTS! THE FOOD THAT REALLY SELLS AND, BACKWARD, YOU KNOW WHAT IT SPELLS!

WHO'S **BACKWARD?**

AH, YES, OKEFENOKEE UNIT! AMERICAL NETWORKS VICE-PREXY HAS AN ON-THE-SPOT AWARD TO MAKE···

VERY GOOD

FOR HIGHEST ACHIEVEMENT! FOUR TWO-MINUTE COMMERCIALS DELIVERED IN A NINE-MINUTE ON-THE-SPOT NEWS EMERGENCY PROGRAM··· GIVEN TO (*WHAT'S YOUR NAME, UNIT CHIEF?*)

BANDWAGGIN! *HERM* BANDWAGGIN

RIGHT! HERM BANDWAGGIN IS NOW AMERICAL NETWORKS *MAN OF THE YEAR!*

BUT *YOU'RE* NOT WITH AMERICAL NETWORKS! YOU'RE *NATIONAL AIR!*

I KNOW! NEVER LOOK A *GIFT HORSE* IN THE MOUTH, PAL···

SNAP

STILL ON THE **EXCITING** SCENE HERE IN OKEFENOKEE WHERE THE **TWO-HEADED FROG** LANDED....

THAT'S DOG! NOT FROG!

RIGHT! FROG IT IS! HERE WE HAVE ONCE AGAIN, FENSTER **MOOP,** THE BELOVED KING OF FOLK SINGERS, WITH HIS BALLAD OF THE TWO-HEADED FROG....

DOG!

♪IN THE **SHADOWS** HERE I LURK♪ SINGING SONGS I CANNOT **SHIRK,** FOR THE MAN WITH WHOM I WORK IS A DOUBLE-HEADED, JF♪

FENSTER!

FIRST, FOLKS, *BEFORE* THE CLOSE OF THAT BALLAD, A BALLAD FROM OUR SPONSOR.... ♪**HAVE YOU USED OUR CREAMLY,** LOVELY, EXTREMELY ♪ ♫SOFT, SWEET AND SEEMLY.... *BARKLE'S AXE HANDLES!?*♫

WHO BLOWED THE FUSE?

FENSTER, I'M AFRAID THE **POWER'S GONE**.... I CAN'T REACH **NATIONAL AIR,** WITH MY **EXCLUSIVE EYE-WITNESS** WORK ANYMORE....

PITY

MAYBE I CAN JUST JIGGLE THIS LITTLE **THINGABOOB** HERE AN'.... *ULK!*

AARGH! STOP THAT!

Double Dome Think

OH, WE WENT TO A LOT OF TROUBLE FOR *THIS* ONE, CHIEF ... AND I THOUGHT OF A GOOD SIDE BAR ... FELLOW SAYS, "THIS DOG WOULD MAKE A GOOD PRESIDENTIAL CANDIDATE".

OTHER GUY SAYS, "YEH, LOOKS LIKE HE'S GOIN' IN BOTH DIRECTIONS AT ONCE WHILE STANDIN' STILL." SURE, OH, *QUOTE ME* ... NOW, HERE'S THE REST OF MY EXTENSIVE, EXCLUSIVE NOTES ON THIS DOG STORY ...

HOWDY, OL' PLURAL PURP

LEMME JUST READ YOU SOME OF THESE *EXCLUSIVE* NOTES ... IT OUGHT TO MAKE A GREAT ON-THE-SPOT, MOBILE UNIT, EYEWITNESS BROADCAST ...

A LOT OF THE STUFF I GOT IS TAKEN DOWN *VERBATIM* AT FIRST HAND FROM EXCLUSIVE EYEWITNESS ACCOUNTS OF THE LANDING OF THE TWO-HEADED DOG DIRECT FROM A SPACE SHIP ...

WHAT'S *THAT?* DID I ACTUALLY SEE THE DOG? NO ... ... HOW DO I KNOW THIS AIN'T A HOAX? WELL, *ACTUALLY*, CHIEF, I *DON'T* ...

BUT THERE'S MORE TO IT THAN *THAT* ... ... IT MAY BE A CASE OF MASS HALLUCINATION ... LIKE THE *FLYING SAUCER* BUSINESS ... YOU KNOW, A BUNCH OF YOKELS GET ALL STEAMED UP ABOUT SOMETHING THAT DOESN'T EXIST ...

WAIT, CHIEF, WE'VE GOT ANOTHER EXPERT EYEWITNESS ON THE TWO-HEADED DOG···· MAYBE HE KNOWS HOW SHE WAGS HER TAIL···· *GOOD EVENING, SIR! YOU'RE FAMILIAR WITH THE TWO-HEADED DOG?*

MAYBE NOT AS MUCH AS YOU'D **THINK**····

YOU WANT TO KNOW HOW SHE **WAGS** HER TAIL?

IN THE FIRST PLACE, SHE AIN'T GOT A ACTUAL TAIL···· SHE GOT ANOTHER **HEAD** ON THAT END···· SO WHEN THE **FIRST HEAD** IS HAPPY AN' AGREEABLE AN' WANTS TO **SHOW** IT····

SHE *TRIES* TO WAG HER TAIL···· SHE GOTTA SHAKE THE SECOND HEAD *"NO"* OR SIDEWAYS, MAKIN' *THAT* HALF DISAGREE WITH THE OTHER, GOIN' *"NO! NO! NO!"*···· IN OTHER WORDS, THIS IS JUS' A SIMPLE, NATURAL, NORMAL, ARBITRARY **TWO-HEADED RUSSIAN DOG**····

GET THAT, CHIEF?

NOW, I ALSO GOT SOME INFORMATION ON THE **SPACE SHIP** WHAT IT BRUNG THE DOG····

YEP···· THIS SPACE SHIP IS A INTERMEDIATE JOB···· TAKES YOU FROM ONE SPOT ON **EARTH** TO ANOTHER AT THE STEADY SPEED OF 25,000 MILES AN HOUR····

FORT MUDGE DAILY MOAN

WHAT DO YOU MEAN... *WHAT GOOD'S THAT?* CAN *YOU* GO AROUND THE WORLD IN A HOUR? ... YOU SAY YOU'D BE RIGHT BACK WHERE YOU STARTED?

AND YOU SAY, BESIDES, YOU'D OF ACTUAL *LOST A HOUR?* MEBBE SO, CHIEF... BUT S'POSE YOU WANTED TO *KILL A HOUR*... THIS WAY'S BETTER'N JUST HANGIN' AROUND THE HOUSE *MOPIN'*, AIN'T IT?

WELL, I GUESS THAT'S ABOUT ALL FROM HERE... ALL THIS OUGHT TO MAKE A NICE EXCLUSIVE BROADCAST FOR YOU TONIGHT, EH, CHET?

OH, THIS ISN'T CHET? HA HA... YOU COULD OF FOOLED *ME*, DAVE... REMEMBER, DAVE, THIS IS A REAL SCOOP... EXCLUSIVE ON *OUR* NETWORK... *WHAT?*

WHAT?! IT'S WALTER?!... WALT, BOY! HOW'D *YOU* GET ON THIS LINE? WALTER, YOU WOULDN'T USE MY EXCLUSIVE, WOULD YOU, WALTIE?... WALTER? WALTER? HELLO? *WALTER!*

WHO GOT ME THIS NUMBER!?

The Whopper Be-rating

LOOK AT IT *THIS* WAY... IF A HUNDRED PEACHES ARE CONSUMED, WE *MUST* CONCLUDE THERE WERE A HUNDRED VIEWERS WATCHING THE TEEVY...

WHY?

BECAUSE WE DO NOT WISH TO *PRESUME* THAT SOME PIGS ATE FIVE OR SIX EACH... WE FEEL ONE APIECE IS PLENTY... IT'S MORE AMERICAN, MORE HONEST... AND *OUR SURVEYS ARE HONEST!*

BUT S'POSE SOME SNEAKY, SECRET PEACH EATER, LIKE AN OLD GRAN'PA, SWIPES A DOZEN AND...

OLD GRAN'PAS DON'T DUMP PITS IN THE GARBAGE ...THEY CHUNKS 'EM UNDER THE BED...

SO WHEN OUR V.P. CHECKS THE GARBAGE CANS AN' FINDS 100 PITS IN ONE OUT OF FOUR, HE *KNOWS* EVERY FOURTH HOUSE HAS **100** TV VIEWERS... THIS WE CALL THE WHOPPER RATING.

YER RIGHT *THERE,* ANYWAY.

IF YOU B'LEEVES TEEVY VIEWERS ARE PEACH EATERS AN' SO COUNTS PEACH PITS TO FIND HOW MANY VIEWERS YOU GOT... HOW'S THE OTHERS DO?

HOW'S THE OTHER NETWORKS COUNT THEIR VIEWERS? WELL, ONE, *WHICH I WILL NOT NAME,* CLAIMED MOST FOLKS ATE MUSHROOMS WHILE WATCHING TEEVY... THEY STOLE OUR *SEED COUNT* PROCESS...

THEIR V.P., MAKIN' A GARBAGE CHECK, FOUND *NO MUSHROOM* SEEDS···SO *HE* COUNTED MUSHMELON SEEDS···

HE MUST OF GOT *BILLIONS!* BUT HE WAS CHEATIN'···

YES··· CLAIMED MORE PEOPLE THAN THERE IS ON *EARTH*··· THE FEDERALS SET HIM OFF THE AIRWAVES FOR A MONTH··· *OH, WE MUST BE ACCURATE, FAIR AND HONEST* WITH OUR WHOPPER RATINGS!

JUS' *GRAND!*

THERE MUST BE SOME OTHER WAY TO COUNT VIEWERS WITHOUT RUMMAGIN' THRU A GARBAGE CAN COUNTIN' *PEACH PITS?*

YES, DURIN' THE *BASEBALL* SEASON OUR V.P. IN CHARGE OF VIEWING RESEARCH COUNTS *EMPTY BEER CANS*···

SURELY A VIEWER DRINKS MORE'N *ONE* CAN OF BEER···

WE LIKE TO THINK OF THE VIEWERS OF *NATIONAL AIR* SHOWS AS NEITHER *PIGS* NOR *DRUNKS*··· NO, WE STILL THINK OF ONE TO A CUSTOMER!

HOW 'BOUT THE *AMERICAL NETWORK?*

MAN! YOU GOT A *ELECTRIFYIN'* THOUGHT THERE··· IT'S POSSIBLE *THEIR* FANS *ARE* PIGS··· ··· PROBABLY DRUNKS, TOO··· THEIR *WHOPPER RATING COULD* BE PADDED··· I'LL ASK THE FEDS TO INVESTIGATE···

JUSTICE GOTTA BE SERVED···

What's in a Name?
Succotash Would Ever Be Succotash

Back Down the Upsy-Daisy

SON, YOU CAN'T DO THAT.... HOW WOULD YOU EVER ELECT THE MAYOR? ... .**DEMOCRATICALLY**, THAT IS?

MAYBE THERE CAN NEVER BE **TRUE PEACE**.... EACH ONE OF US IS SO MIXED HE'S USUALLY AT ODDS WITH HIS OWNSELF....

TAKE THAT TWO-HEADED RUSSIAN DOG .... ONE HEAD WOULD NOD, HAPPY AND AFFIRMATIVE, WHICH WOULD WAG HIS TAIL SIDEWAYS ON WHICH END WAS HIS OTHER HEAD WHICH WOULD SHAKE ITSELF SIDEWAYS MEANIN' *"NYET"*....

NO, CHURCHY.... IT'S TOO BAD, BUT BASICALLY, EVERY MAN IS USUAL AT WAR WITH **HIMSELF**.

YEAH, BUT I DON'T GO PULLIN' GUNS ON MYSELF AN' FORCE ME UP AGAINST A WALL!

Part Four

Campaign and Counterpaign

Stump the lands,
   North and South!
Shake the hands,
   speech and sing!
Put your foot
   in your mouth,
And your hat is
   in the ring!

The Future Is the Perfect Tense
of the Past

I'M GONE OVER AN' SHOW ALBERT AN' POGO HOW OL' **FENSTER MOOP** CAN FORECAST THE **FUTURE**...

DON'T LEAVE ME ALONE AT A TIME LIKE THIS!

OOMP?

DON'T YOU REALIZE THAT IF 1964 WERE TEN DAYS OLDER, TODAY WOULD BE *FRIDAY*, THE **THIRTEENTH**?!

IT WOULD **NOT!**

IT WOULD BE *MONDAY;* **MONDAY!**

WORSE! THAT MEANS FRIDAY, THE THIRTEENTH, WOULD COME ON BLUE MONDAY..."*SPOILIN'* THE *WHOLE* WEEK!

BEFORE I GO INTO *PRE*-DICTING THINGS I GOTTA TELL YOU A MEMORABLE STORY TOLE ME STOP ME IF YOU HEARN THIS IT SEEM TWO FELLOWS...

STOP

ONE WAS COUNTIN' THE PEOPLE OF THE COUNTRY WHICH HE THUNK WAS A GREAT THING TH' OTHER'N SAY HE MAKIN' A BOMB WHICH GONNA BLOW UP ALL WITHIN **DEADSHOT**...

GURG

88

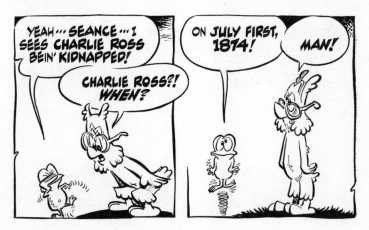

The Brake on the Coffee Breakdown

NO! NO! IT MEANS THAT A WHOLE NEW LABOR FORCE CAN BE EXPEDITED TO FILL **COFFEE BREAKS** THE CLOCK AROUND!

FILLIN' IN THE **EMPTY** FIFTEEN MINUTESES?

YEP... THE ORNERY WORKER GONNA WORK A **45** MINUTE HOUR... **WHOOSH!** IN COME HIS COFFEE BREAKER... HE DRINKS COFFEE FOR OUR MAN! YOU KNOW WHERE THIS'LL **LEAD**?

TO THE HOSPITAL WITH ACID STOMACHS...

WHEN YOU INVENTED THE **FORTY-FIVE MINUTE HOUR,** I BET YOU DIN'T REALIZE WHAT YOU WAS **OPENIN' UP!**

CANS OF COFFEE?

NOT ONLY THAT, BUT A WHOLE NEW FIELD OF WORKERS... THE **COFFEE BREAKER**... HE COMES IN AN' TAKES A FIFTEEN MINUTE COFFEE BREAK FOR YOU EVERY HOUR ON THE HALF-HOUR...

S'POSE THIS BOY DRINKS TWO CUPS OF COFFEE EVERY HOUR FOR YOU, THAT'S SIXTEEN CUPS OF COFFEE...

AN' **DONUTS**... I LIKES DONUTS WITH MY COFFEE... HE GOTTA EAT **TWO, THREE DONUTS!**

THAT WOULD HAFTA BE **NEE-**GOTIATED. IT AIN'T IN THE CONTRACT THAT WAY...

I **KNOWED** THE DONUT CLAUSE WOULD HAVE A COUPLE **HOLES** IN IT!

THE THING WE GOTTA DO IS *ORGANIZE* ALL THE COFFEE BREAKERS!

AN' US WILL HEAD THE UNION?

RIGHT··· USIN' YOUR IDEA OF A *FORTY-FIVE MINUTE HOUR*··· *EVERYBODY* WORKIN' GETS EIGHT COFFEE BREAKS A DAY··· THAT MEANS THE *WORKER* GETS A ASSISTANT WHO DRINKS HIS *COFFEE* FOR HIM!

THIS GUY, OF COURSE, WORKS FOR *THREE OR FOUR MEN*··· SO HE'S BUSY DRINKIN' COFFEE ALL DAY··· THAT MEANS ONE COFFEE BREAKER FOR EVERY FOUR WORKERS!

SO WE TAKES OUR MEN FROM THE RANKS OF THE *UNEMPLOYED*··· ONCE AGAIN, THE *FULL DINNER PAIL!*

THAT AIN'T ALL WHAT'LL BE FULL···

THIS PLAN FOR THE FORTY-FIVE-MINUTE HOUR··· WHICH WILL LEAD TO THE *HIRING* OF *THOUSANDS OF COFFEE BREAKERS*···

···IS THE SOLUTION TO *UNEMPLOYMENT*··· THE GUMMINT LOOKIN' FOR A CURE ···YOU AN' ME WILL TRAIN THESE COFFEE DRINKERS, WHO'RE GONNA HELP THE REGULAR WORKERS DRINK THEIR COFFEE DURING EIGHT DAILY COFFEE BREAKS···

The Loom of Weaving Candidates

YOU DON'T THINK GOIN' TO CONGERSMAN JUMPHREY FROG WOULD DO ANY GOOD?

IF YOU MEAN TO PUT ACROSS THE 45 MINUTE HOUR, **NO!**

YOU FERGETS! HE'S UP FOR RE-ELECTION.... DOES HE WANT MY VOTE OR NOT?

YOUR VOTE?! YOU AIN'T VOTED SINCE **NONETEEN-NOUGHT-NONE!**

NONE-THE-BELOVED-LESS, I IS HAD A **UNCANNY** EYE FOR THE **WINNING** CANDIDATE....

TRUE TRUE....

MATTER OF FACT, YOU IS HAD *TWO* OF 'EM.... ONE GUY LOOKED INTO YOUR PEEPERS AN' SAID YOU HAD THE **UNCANNIEST** PAIR OF ORBS ON RECORD....GAVE HIM THE HEEB-JEEBS.

COME BACK HERE!

OL' CHURCHY DON'T B'LEEVE **CONGERSMAN FROG** IS THE MAN TO TAKE OUR 45-MINUTE-HOUR BILL TO....

NOW, I IS *ON THE SIDE* OF CONGERSMAN FROG....OL' JUMPHREY GOT MORE ON THE BALL, *'CAUSE* HE'S **IN**.... I B'LEEVES IN THE **INCUMBENT**.... RATHER'N THE **MAYBE-AIN'T-INCOMIN'**.... BUT *CHURCHY!* WHAT'S *HE* SAY....?

"CONGERSMAN FROG IS MASTERED THE THIRTY MINUTE HOUR AND THE SIX MONTH YEAR! HE VOTES BY MAIL··· WITH ALWAYS SOMETHIN' DUE ON IT···

"HE'S THE MASTER OF X SKILLS BECAUSE IT'S THE ONLY MARK HE CAN MAKE IN THIS WORLD: X!" ··· *OH!* HEH-LO THERE, JUMPHREY···

WELL!!

SO! YOU'RE INSULTIN' ME BEHIND MY BACK!? *CALLIN' ME A NUMB-SKULL···UNFIT FOR MY JOB!*

ME? NOT ME!

YOU SAID, "CONGERSMAN FROG IS MASTERED THE **THIRTY MINUTE HOUR** AND THE **SIX MONTH YEAR**··· HE VOTES BY **MAIL** WITH ALWAYS *SOMETHING* DUE ON IT!"

NOT ME! I WAS *QUOTIN'!*

QUOTIN'?! A LIKELY STORY··· I DON'T BELIEVE A WORD OF IT··· *WHO WAS YOU QUOTIN'?*

SO HELP ME··· I DON'T WANNA *SQUEAL* ON A PAL··· WILD HORSES COULDN'T DRAG IT OUTEN ME··· *CHURCHY LA FEMME* IT WAS···

LA FEMME, HUH? THE KID'S GOT TALENT··· GREAT *SPEECH WRITER*··· WONDER IF HE'D CHANGE SIDES IF THE *PRICE* WAS *RIGHT?*

The Unreason of Reason

I'VE JUST COME FROM A VERY REFRESHING DISCUSSION WITH THE CANDIDATE...

WHAT CANDIDATE? L B AND J?

NOPE....OUR MAN....GOOD OL' CONGERSMAN JUMPHREY FROG....HE GONNA RUN FOR CONGERS AGAIN....WANTS YOU TO RUN FOR PRESIDENT WITH HIM....SAYS YOU'LL RIDE IN ON HIS COATTAILS....

WANNA KNOW SOMETHIN'? JUMPHREY AIN'T GOT NO COAT!

THE ONLY PARTY I KNOW WHICH CONGERSMAN FROG WAS A MEMBER OF WAS BROKE UP BY THE SHERIFF AT 4 A.M. OF A SUNDAY MORNING···· *WHAT'S HE STAND FOR ANYWAY?*

HE STANDS FOR PLENTY···· YOU EVER SEE HIS WIFE AN' IN-LAWS?

CONGERSMAN FROG GOT A *BROAD PLATFORM*···ONE WHAT WILL INCLUDE SOMETHIN' FOR VOTERS OF *EVERY STRIPE!*

YOU MEAN HE GOT *TIGERS, ZEBRAS* AN' *JAILBIRDS* GOIN' FOR HIM? HOW'S HE STAND ON THE ISSUES? ···· TAKE *CAPITAL*····

HE'LL DO IT ···· HE AIN'T BASHFUL.

NOT ONLY IS HE FOR CAPITAL ··· HE'S FOR *LABOR!* WITH A *CAPITAL EL, BOW!*

HE'S FOR LABOR? *NOT HIS OWN,* I BETCHA ····

WELL, *COME, COME!* WE AIN'T *ALL* PERFECT····

The Lonesomeness of the Fellow Runner

If you promise to listen, I'll give you some advice-- It'll come in handy if you become President----

LOOK, I DON'T EVEN PROMISE TO *RUN*---- LET ALONE LISTEN!

First of all, you must be strong! Them other fellows threaten us with *rockets*---- Claim they'll annihilate us first----*zounds!* If they do, do you know what we'll do to them?

IF WE'RE ANNIHILATED, WHAT *CAN* WE DO?

Arm-chair general!

As I understand it, you ran at the same time as Adlai, last time you ran?

YEP, AN' THE TIME AFORE *THAT*, TOO---- GREAT RUNNING MATE!

Running mate? You didn't run with him, did you? You both ran on the same ticket?

ONLY IN A WAY---WE EACH RUN ON A ROUND-TRIP TICKET---- WOUND UP WHERE WE STARTED!

110

Frogs Run a Jumpy Campaign

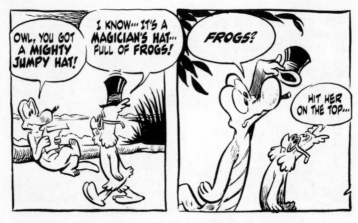

The Upside Down Hour Glass
of Gummint

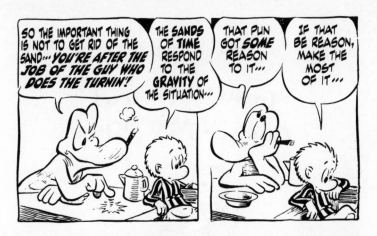

Part Five

Images and Other Mirages

How do I look
    when I'm dancing?
Out in the public
    and prancing?

How do I look
    while staging a show
For anyone watching····
    ····or shouldn't I know?

Not Worth the Public Image
of a Tax Collector

BY JING! IT'S A SCANDAL... HERE THEY REDUCES TAXES FOR EVERYBODY BUT A COUPLE SELECTED GROUPS! *DISCRIMINATION!*

GROUPS LIKE WHO?

GROUPS LIKE BATS, BIG IN RADAR; BURGLARS; MICE... AFTER ALL WE DID TO ADVANCE CANCER...

IT *DO* SEEM A POPULAR THING TO REDUCE TAXES... IF THEY KEPT 'EM UP IT'D OF ONLY LED TO TROUBLE...

HOW?

WELL, HERE'S EVERYBODY PAYIN' FOR A *TRIP TO THE MOON* AN' HOW MANY'D GET TO GO? OH, THERE'D BE COMPLAINTS, I'LL TELL YA...

BY ME, IF I WAS CHOSE.

THERE'S ONLY *ONE* WAY TO RUN A TAX PROGRAM THAT SATISFIES *EVERYBODY*...

HOW?

THE GUMMINT PAYS TAXES TO THE PEOPLE... EVERY YEAR YOU GET A NICE FAT CHECK... ...EVEN THEN THERE'D BE CARPERS... 85% WOULD CLAIM THEY SHOULD BE IN A HIGHER BRACKET...

How could it occur to you to identify Whistler's Mother with a stove-pipe hat?

SO HELP ME, IT'S A LOT EASIER'N IDENTIFYIN' *YOU* WITH A *HONEST MAN!*

All I'm trying to do for some candidate, you, me, Pogo, (who knows?) is to create an image---

An image of honesty, stature and of impeccable dignity!

COME ON! A IMAGE AIN'T THE SAME AS THE McCOY, DEAC!

Sirrah, you sully the public trend----Our proud and ancient people in this day are a-buzz with imagery! Our national image; our foreign image; our---

DEAC, ALL I KNOW IS THAT ANOTHER **PROUD** AND **ANCIENT PEOPLE** FOUND IMAGES NOT WORTH A PLUGGED NICKEL WHEN THE HEAT WAS ON··· EVEN WHEN THEY WAS MADE OF GOLD···

Penny Panty Ante

A LADY PRESIDENT WOULD NO NEVER HAVE **THREE MILLION** SOLDIERS TO PUSH **ONE STUPIDS** BUTTON TO START BOMBS!

MESSE THEY GOT THREE MILLION BUTTONS.

ON PANTS, MAYBE YES, OTHERELSE TO START WAR ··· **ONE BUTTON** ··· *ONE, COUNT HIM, ONE FINGER!*

ONE FINGER TO ONE BUTTON IS THE PREFERRED TECHNIQUE, YER RIGHT ··· SOME FOLKS **MIGHT USE A THUMB** ···

SO WHY THREE MILLION THUMBS ··· NO, *SIX* ·· TIED UP?

YOU GOT A **POINT** ··· IT'S JUST AS EASY TO **OPEN A WAR,** NOW, AS IT IS TO OPEN A NEW BRIDGE, LIGHT THE WHITE HOUSE LAWN CHRISTMAS TREE OR START UP A **SUPER MARKET** ···

TECHNIQUES IS IMPROVE.

WHY? WHY? WHY 3,000,000 MEN IN STANDING ARMIES TO START PUSH-BUTTON WAR? ··· THESE MEN COULD BE DO SOMETHING USEFUL ···

WELL, THEY'RE A SAFETY FACTOR ···

YOU LINE UP 3,000,000 MEN AND HAVE 'EM *PASS THE WORD* ··· YOU KNOW, *"OKAY, HARRY, PUSH THE BUTTON!"* *"PUSH THE BUTTON, MARY!"* *"PUSH THE BUTTON, MILTON!"*

127

AN' WE ARE COMPARATIVELY **UNKNOWN**.... NOBODY KNOWS WE X'S ARE TIRED OF HAND-OUTS.... WE WANNA BE THE ONES TO BE HANDIN' OUT!

FEEL FREE... WE'LL COME TO **YOUR** PICNIC IF YOU'LL COME TO OURS...

YOU'RE TRYIN' TO PUT US X'S IN A **UNFAIR** POSITION!

HOW COME IT'S **UNFAIR** FOR US TO GO TO THE **BLUE MUSLIN** PICNIC IF YOU COMES TO OURS?

YOU GOT A **GOIN'-PICNIC** .... WE AIN'T!

WELL, OKAY, SKIP *THAT*... WHAT'S SO MUSLINNY ABOUT YOU NEW PEOPLE CALLED THE X'S? WHY'S **YOU THE BLUE MUSLINS?**

FERD! OH, FERD!

MAN! A **BLUE MUSLIN HOOD!** WHAT'S HE? A K·K···UH... I MEAN, A X·X·X?

FERD! FERD! OVER HERE, I SAY, FERD ....**YOU'RE MISSING THE RUNWAY!**

I DON'T CARE WHAT COLOR HOOD YOU THROWS OVER YOUR HEAD... YOU CAN'T REALLY SEE WHERE YOU'RE GOIN'....

FERD, BOY!

A Medium Day in June,
Well Done and Rare

133

137

The Soft Unders of the Top Dog

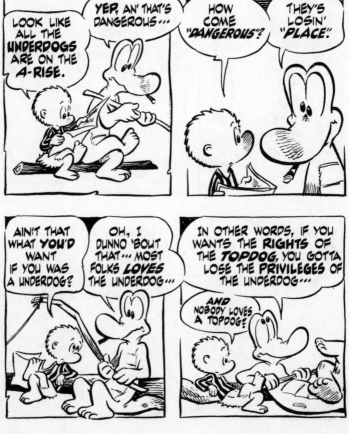

142

This Country Needs
a Cheaper 5¢ Cigar

Part Six

The Campaign Winds Up and... Let's Go

Best round of the fight
    is the very last ONE,
When you're either the
    winner or able to run.

The Square Grass Root of Nothing

New Problems and Old Solutions

You're **RIGHT**, Tammananny! *Just thinking of* ☆ !! **NEW PROBLEMS** is a PROBLEM!

The **NEW PROBLEMS PARTY** offers a CHOICE OF PROBLEMS *BUT* WHAT *ARE* THEY? 👉 **NO ME·TOO·ISM** here! *We will*, CREATIVELY, FEARLESSLY, GLADLY ☆ **DISCOVER NEW** ⇨ **PUZZLES**!

NOW, AS I SAY, I *have* HAD MY EYE ON 👉 *you!* FOR CANDIDATE ☆ **BUT** the *REQUIREMENTS* of the new party force **ME** to make a change ⟿

TO WHOM?

ME DUTY CALLS! ☆☆☆☆☆

GOOD FOR YOU ··· YOU JUST PROVIDED THE **NEW PROBLEMS PARTY** WITH ITS FIRST PROBLEM.

THE **NEW PROBLEMS PARTY** ☆ will have a **KITCHEN CABINET** TO 👉 COOK UP *NEW PROBLEMS!*

HERE'S A KITCHEN, LET'S GO····

POGO

WE'LL form a ☆**BRAIN** ☆ **BUSTER** GROUP! *WE* won't BORROW PROBLEMS! *NO* ME·TOO·ISM 👉**FRESH** BLOOD!! ☆

155

The Under Cover Candidate

THAT'S FINE, SIR! JUST ONE MORE···· DON'T FORGET TO LET **GO** OF YOUR **TOES** **THIS** TIME, SIR····

NOW, HOW ABOUT A FEW **PUSH-UPS?** ····OR DO YOU HAVE ANY **DOGS** WITH LONG EARS? ···· I SAY, SIR, **SPEAK TO ME, SIR**····

WHAT DO THEY THINK THEY'RE **DOING?**

NO CANDIDATE HE···! AND **YOU'VE** BEEN SHOOTING HIM **!!** **POGO,** THE **STRIPED POSSUM,** IS OUR MAN···· **NEVER FAILS RESEARCH,** FLASHBULB!

THEY DID **THIS** TIME, PENCILS····

YOU MEAN OUR POLLS ARE **WRONG**···· THAT **POGO** THERE IS **NOT** THE CANDIDATE?

YEP

OUR POLLS **WRONG!** INCREDIBLE! A DISLOYAL REMARK···· I'LL HAVE TO TAKE YOU HOME IN **CHAINS,** LENSCAP····

FATSO IS THE CANDIDATE 'CAUSE I USED ALL MY **FILM** ON HIM···· I THUNK **HE WAS THE STORY!**

SO, HE'S THE STORY WE **GOT,** HE'S THE STORY WE USE···· **NEWSLIFE** GOT NO TIME TO FOOL AROUND, TYPO!

WELL, IT CERTAINLY **SIMPLIFIES** THE DEMOCRATIC PROCESS····

157

* RHYMES WITH WORCESTERSHIRE

The Crystal Boll and
Pop Goes the Weevil

HERE WE IS, ALL GEARED UP AND **NO CUSTOMERS** FOR US POLLSTERS OF THE PUBLIC PULSE.

HERE COMES A PUBLIC NOW... HOW'S **YOUR** PULSE, PUBLIC?

149 DEGREES FARENHEIT...

WE'S IN THE POLL BUSINESS... HOW DOES **YOU** POLL?

NIX... THAT'S MY GAME!

A **EXPERT?**

YEP... I BEEN BOWLIN' FOR YEARS. HAND ME THE BALL THERE AND I'LL GIVE YOU A FEW POINTERS... STEP INTO THE ALLEY.

WE'RE NOT **BOLSTERS,** WE'RE **POLLSTERS,** BOLL WEEVIL!

YEAH!

NEXT TIME, BRONOUNCE YOUR "P'S"!

AHA! **THERE** HE IS... A MAN IN DESPERATE NEED OF OUR **PREE-DICTIONS**... DOUBTLESS, YOU'D LIKE A RESULT OF OUR LATEST POLL, SIR...

NOW, WHAT **KIND** OF A POLL RESULT WOULD YOU LIKE? A 35¢ JOB, HALF A BUCK, SEVENTY-FIVE CENTS OR A DOLLAR?

WHAT'S THE DIFFERENCE?

One to Get Set,
Two to Get Ready,
Three to Consider,
and NONE to Go

Snakes Do Everything No Hands

169

The Vice of the Turtle

No Confidence in the Confidential

174

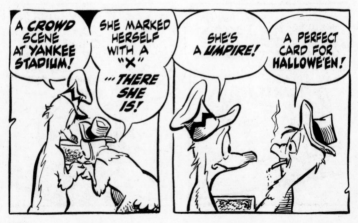

The Votary Public

FIRST ONTO BUS FOR AIRPORT, (FOR BEST SEAT); FIRST ONTO AIRCRAFT, (LIKEWISE); FIRST TO ALL MEALS, (REASONS UNKNOWN); FIRST TO BED ···

WASN'T HE EVER LAST?

YES ··· AND IT COST US ··· HE WAS USUALLY THE LAST ONE TO GET UP ··· 4 P.M.

DIDN'T P.T. EVER MAKE IT TO AN EVENT AT THE OLYMPICS?

WELL, SIR, THEREIN LIES A TALE AT WHICH YOU'LL THRILL WITH *PRIDE!*

IT WAS THE LAST DAY! P.T. WAS UP BETIMES ··· JAW SET, HE CROUCHED FOR A START ··· OFF HE SPED ··· SPECTATORS STOOD TRANSFIXED ··· HE WAS TRULY A ROCKET ··· AN ARROW TO THE TARGET ···

GASPING! WEAVING WITH FATIGUE ··· *HE FELL* ··· ONLY INCHES BEHIND THE TRAIN AS IT PULLED AWAY FOR THE STADIUM ···

HE EVEN *MISSED THE TRAIN?*

DO YOU MEAN HE FELL IN BACK OF THE TRAIN?

GREAT PRESENCE OF MIND THERE! YOU GOTTA ADMIT IT WAS BETTER THAN FALLING IN *FRONT* OF THE TRAIN!

Part Seven

The Wriggle
of the Wreath

Of all the dances
    known to men,
The Twist, the Bump,
    the Dying Hen,
The Crash, the Crazy
    Caterpiggle,
Best *for me's*
    the Christmas Wiggle.

Unemployment on the Worm Beat

TAKE **CRICKETS**··· THEY USED TO GET A LOT OF WORK, OUTDOOR TYPE···NOW SOMEBODY WANTS TO HEAR A CRICKET, HE TURNS THE **RADIO** ON TO A **SWAMP PROGRAM**···

AN' IT'S FULL OF **MECHANICAL CHIRPS** SUPPLIED BY A VICE-PRESIDENT WALKIN' AROUND IN **SQUEAKY SHOES**···THOUSANDS OF CRICKETS OUT OF WORK··· **DISGRACEFUL!**

SOMEHOW MY HEART HAS NEVER BLED FOR CRICKETS···

IF THE **BAIT BUSINESS** IS A FROST, WHY NOT GO INTO THE **APPLE GAME?**

WELL···

WORKIN' IN APPLES AIN'T EXACTLY WHAT WE'RE CUT OUT FOR···IT'S EASIER EATIN' **DIRT** THAN **APPLES**···

WITH APPLES YOU GOTTA HAVE JAWS LIKE UNTO A **RHINOCERWURST.**

HOW ABOUT **COCOONIN' UP** AN' GOIN' INTO THE **BUTTERFLY DODGE?**

WHAT!? ALL THAT **FLYIN' ABOUT** AN' HORSIN' AROUND BUTTERCUPS? MAN, IT'D MAKE MY HEAD SWIM!

YOU GUYS ARE JUST HARD TO PLEASE.

Automation
Will Never Replace the Snake

186

WELL, I WAS WORKIN' IN THE NEXT TENT AS THE DANCING COMPANION OF **LITTLE FATIMA**.... I COME OUT OF A BOTTLE WHEN SHE PLAYED "**THE CHARGE OF THE BUMBLE BEE**" ON TISSUE PAPER AND COMB....

THEN SHE GOT A BOTTLE OF HER **OWN** AND STARTED SEEIN' SNAKES FOR **FREE**. NATURALLY, I WAS REQUESTED TO VACATE THE PREMISES....

DIN'T EVEN GET A GOLD WATCH?

SEE, I CAN STILL DO A LITTLE SCAT DANCE.... HUM A BIT OF "**THE CHARGE OF THE BUMBLE BEE**"

HMM HMTY HM HM

THAT'S NOT QUITE THE WAY IT GOES.... YOU LEFT OUT THE **SEMI-DEMI-QUIVER-QUAVER** IN THE **FOURTH** MOVEMENT....

SUE ME

WHEN OL' SAM SAW HE WAS STUCK WITH A **STIFF SNAKE**, HE WENT LOOKIN' FOR A REPLACEMENT....

COULDN'T HE OF **OILED** THE MACHINE COBRA?

OH, THE MECHANICAL SERPENT WAS WELL OILED. NO, HE WAS JUST **WOUND** TOO TIGHT. SO SAM ASKED ME TO SUBSTITUTE....

THE **FIRST** CASE OF A HUMAN REPLACING A MACHINE!

190

A Short and Merry Christmas